Can you find...
1001 Dinosaurs
and other things?

igloobooks

Can you find 1001 Dinosaur things?

ROAR! Welcome to a dinosaur adventure! There's all sorts of things going on in Dinoland, from Roger Raptor's birthday bash to the Meteor Music Festival. Each picture in this book has lots of different and interesting things for you to search and find. In fact, there are over 1000 things to find in Dinoland! Terry T-Rex and Stegosaurus Stan are in each picture, so you need to find them first. Then each page has little pictures to show you what else you need to search for, from Pre-historic Pop to Sabre Tooth Tigers!

Terry T-Rex

Stegosaurus Stan

Let's have a practice. Can you spot Terry T-Rex and Stegosaurus Stan? Once you've found them, see if you can spot these items as well in the picture on the opposite page.

1 Aeroplane

5 Squirrels

10 Frogs

Carnivore Cafe

It's the weekend and that's when Carnivore Café is at its busiest! See if you can find Terry T-Rex and Stegosaurus Stan amongst all the other customers.

Carnivore Cafe

Specials:
Pre-historic Pie
Dino Dumplings
Swampy Soup

Dish of the day:
Fried Fossils

1 Menu Board

2 Aprons

3 Chef Hats

4 Plants

5 Steaks

6 Mugs of Hot Chocolate

7 Menus

8 Salt Shakers

9 Bottles of Ketchup

10 Snails

20 Forks

Fossil Beach

It's a sunny day on Fossil Beach and all of the dinosaurs are having fun in the sun.
Once you've found Stegosaurus Stan and Terry T-Rex, try spotting all of the other things, too!

 **4 Rainbow Fish**

 5 Lizards

 6 Rubber Rings

 7 Crabs

Can you find all of these other items on the beach, too?

1 Footprint

2 Pterodactyls

3 Bone-shaped Surfboards

8 Sun Hats

9 Umbrellas

10 Ice creams

20 Sea Shells

Pre-historic Party

It's Roger Raptor's birthday. He's having a big party and everyone's invited. Can you spot Terry T-Rex and Stegosaurus Stan amongst the guests?

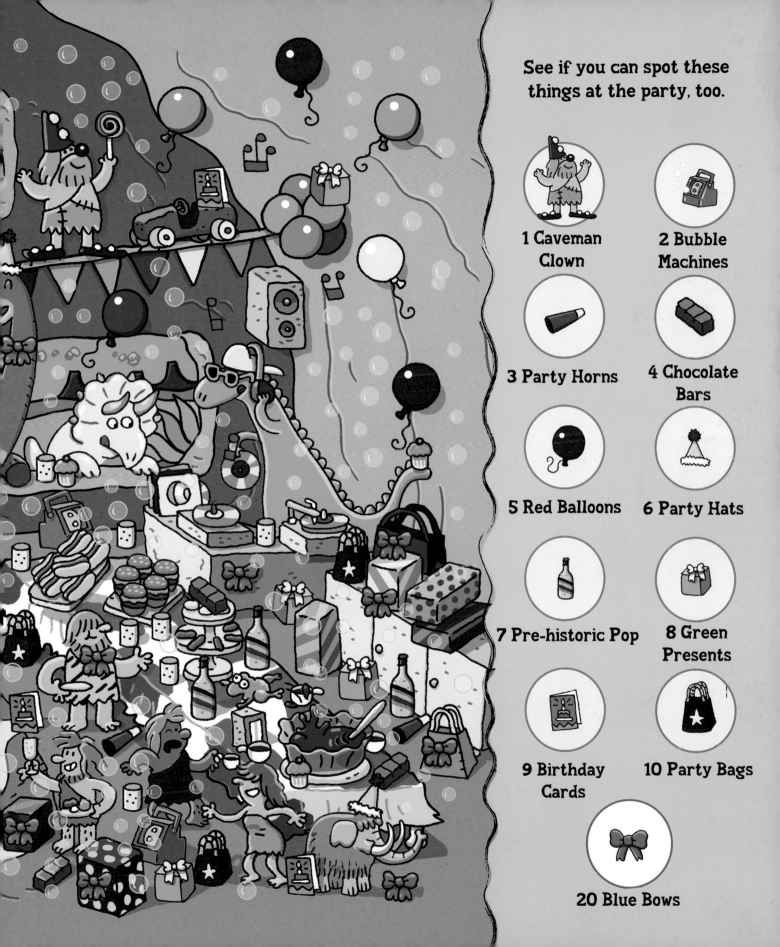

See if you can spot these things at the party, too.

1 Caveman Clown

2 Bubble Machines

3 Party Horns

4 Chocolate Bars

5 Red Balloons

6 Party Hats

7 Pre-historic Pop

8 Green Presents

9 Birthday Cards

10 Party Bags

20 Blue Bows

Meteor Music Festival

It's the annual music festival and this year The
Bone Bashers are playing a gig.
Can you see if Terry T-Rex and Stegosaurus
Stan are amongst the crowd?

Can you find these things
at the festival, too?

1 Drum Kit   2 Tents

3 Microphones   4 Blankets

5 Speakers   6 Cell Phones

7 Glow Worms   8 Band T-Shirts

9 Money Pouches   10 Welly Boots

20 Love Hearts

The Reptile Races

Every year the dinosaurs and cavemen have a sports day. This year there are even more events! Can you spot Terry T-Rex and Stegosaurus Stan?

4 Shot Puts   **5 Stop Watches**   **6 Javelins**   **7 Blue Shorts**

When you've found Terry and Stan, see if you can find these things as well.

1 Bike

2 Trampolines

3 Whistles

8 Worms

9 Kit Bags

10 Bottles of Pop

20 Orange Segments

Fossil Fair

Everyone's been excited about the fair coming to town and now it's here! Can you spot where Terry T-Rex and Stegosaurus Stan are?

See if you can spot these things as the fair as well.

1 Arcade Machine

2 Ticket Machines

3 Teddy Bears

4 Gold Fish

5 Windmills

6 Lanterns

7 Hotdogs

8 Golden Tickets

9 Candyfloss

10 Boxes of Popcorn

20 Popsicles

Jurassic Jumble

Lots of dinosaurs love shopping at the local market. See if you can spot Terry T-Rex and Stegosaurus Stan in the crowd?

4 Footballs

5 Cricket Bats

6 Banana Signs

7 Yellow Books

Now you've found Terry and Stan, see if you can spot these things.

1 Chalk Board

2 Tennis Rackets

3 Pineapples

8 Balls of Wool

9 Prawns

10 Jars of Marbles

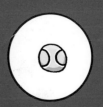

20 Tennis Balls

Herbivore Hill

It's been snowing and all of the dinosaurs and cavemen are ready with their skis and sledges at Herbivore Hill. Can you see what Terry T-Rex and Stegosaurus Stan are doing in the snow?

See if you cans pot these on Herbivore Hill, too.

1 Yeti

2 Snowboarding Mice

3 Green Snowboards

4 Tobogans

5 Red Goggles

6 Blue Hats

7 Stripy Scarfs

8 Yellow Gloves

9 Flags

10 Big Snowballs

20 Snowflakes

Asteroid Academy

Everyone has so much fun at Asteroid Academy!
Can you spot where Terry T-Rex and Stegosaurus
Stan are?

4 Pencil Holders

5 Pieces of Chalk

6 Calculators

7 Rulers

Can you find these things in the classroom, as well?

1 Clock

2 Globes

3 Blue Satchels

8 Pairs of scissors

9 Paper planes

10 Pens

20 Apples

Triassic Rock

The dinosaurs are having fun painting at Triassic Rock, even if it is a little messy! Can you find Terry T-Rex and Stegosaurus Stan amongst the painters?

Once you've spotted Terry and Stan, try finding these things, too.

1 Statue

2 Sloths

3 Bowls of fruit

4 Easels

5 Paint Rollers

6 Pallettes

7 Aprons

8 Water Pots

9 Brushes

10 Paint Prints

20 Paint Tubes

Well done! You found everything in Dinoland! Now go back and see if you can find each of these extra items in every picture, too.

1 Nest

1 Triceratops

1 Baby Dinosaur

1 Club

1 Car

1 Fire

1 Spider

1 Caveman with Polkadot Tunic

1 Saber Tooth Tiger

1 Woolly Mammoth

1 Cave Painting

Wow! You found them all! How closely were you looking though? Do you know which picture each of these items in?

10 Beach Bags

10 Cupcakes

10 Toffee Apples

10 Burgers

10 Mosquitoes

10 Note pads

10 Ladybugs

10 Candles

10 Penguins

10 Trolleys